SK063865555
7·95.

# CHESTER'S EASIEST
# CHRISTMAS MUSIC

## Seventeen songs & piano solos for Christmas
## by Carol Barratt

*This book is dedicated to Ann and Tom Barratt - enjoy yourselves!*

The chord symbols suggested have been chosen to suit the solo melody and do not always correspond with the harmony of the arrangements, as importance has been placed on interesting left hand accompaniments using simple hand positions.

This book © Copyright 1994 Chester Music
Order No. CH60144. ISBN 0-7119-4310-9

**Illustrations by Sarah Lenton**
© 1994 Sarah Lenton.

Music processed by Barnes Music Engraving.
Printed in the United Kingdom by Caligraving Limited, Thetford, Norfolk.

**Chester Music Limited**
(A division of Music Sales Limited)
8/9 Frith Street, London W1V 5TZ.

# PAT-A-PAN

The *staccato* notes in the left hand are important as they imitate the sound of the drum, or tambourin\*, which would have accompanied this ancient French Carol.

**Burgundian Traditional Carol**

**Moderately – not fast**

\* The tambourin was a small elongated drum which hung from the shoulders. It was originally played with the hands.

# GO, TELL IT ON THE MOUNTAIN

**American Traditional**

# CHRISTMAS PASTORALE

Valentin Rathgeber
(1682 – 1750)

# CHRISTMAS IS COMING

English Traditional

# WHAT SHALL I GIVE TO THE CHILD IN THE MANGER?

**Words: Angela Diller and Kate Stearn-Page**

**Music: Spanish Carol**

2. What shall I give to the child in the manger?
What shall I give to the beautiful boy?
Garlands of flowers to twine in his fingers,
Cherries so big for the child to enjoy.
Tam-pa-tam-tam when the cherries have ripened,
Tam-pa-tam-tam they will add to his joy.

# GATHERED ROUND THE CHRISTMAS TREE

**Adapted from
Vladimir Rebikov
(1866 – 1920)**

✛ = Coda Sign: Second time round, jump from this sign to the same sign at the end of the piece to complete the music.

# IL EST NÉ

**French Traditional Carol**

He is born, the di-vine Christ Child, Greet Him with gai-ly re-sound-ing pipe and drum,
Il est né, le di-vin en-fant. Jou-ez haut-bois ré-son-ez mus-et-tes,

He is born, the di-vine Christ Child, Join in song, for the Lord has come.
Il est né, le di-vin en-fant, Chant-ons tous son a-vé-ne-ment.

Proph-ets wise had fore-told His birth, Pledg-ing peace to all men on earth,
De-puis plus de quat-tre mille ans, Nous le pro-met-tai-ent les proph-èt-es,

Filled with hope, men be-gan to pray, Till His com-ing this hap-py day.__
De-puis plus de quat-tre mille ans, Nous at-tend-i-ons cet heur-eux temps.

*If you are learning how to use the sustaining pedal, this piece
would be ideal for practising 'legato' pedalling to give a fuller
sound to the chords.

# Variation on an old English Carol
# I SAW THREE SHIPS

Bring out the tune in the top half of your right hand, listening carefully to the balance between the parts.

Carol Barratt

\* Change the pedal every half bar ie.
(Bars 1 and 2, whole bar for each pedal)

$\left(\dfrac{6}{8}\right)$ ♩  ♪  ♩  ♪  etc.

# THE LITTLE DRUMMER BOY

**Words: Katherine K. Davis**

**Czech Carol Tune**

To lay be - fore the king, pa - rum pum pum pum, rum pum pum pum,

rum pum pum pum. So to hon-our him, pa -

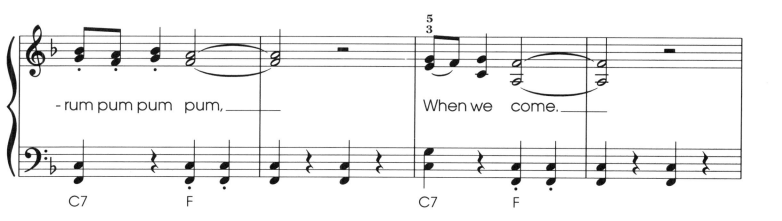

- rum pum pum pum, When we come.

# JINGLE BELLS

**James Pierpont**

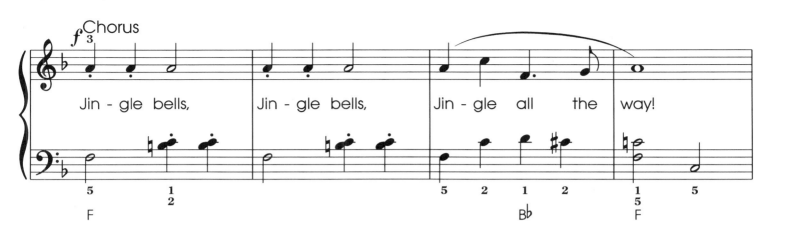

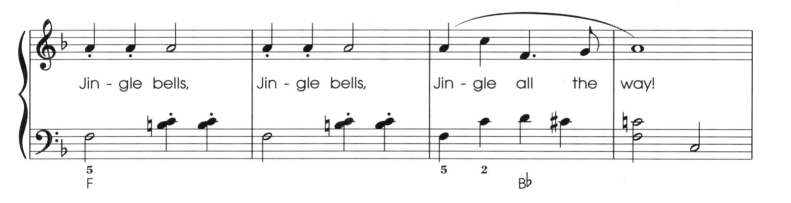

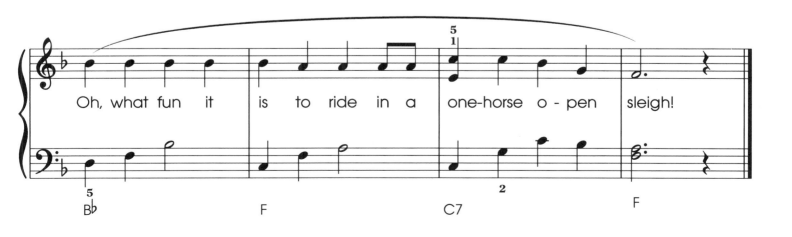

# THE VIRGIN MARY
# HAD A BABY BOY

**West Indian Spiritual**

He came from the glo - ry, He came from the glo-rious king-dom.

C7      F   Bb6   C7      F   C7   F

Oh___ yes, be-liev - er! Oh___ yes, be-liev - er!

Bb      F      Bb      F

He came from the glo - ry, He came from the glo-rious king-dom.

C7      F   Bb6   C7      F   C7   F

2. The angels sang when the baby born,
The angels sang when the baby born,
The angels sang when the baby born,
And proclaimed him the Saviour Jesus.
*He came from the glory...*

3. The wise men saw where the baby born,
The wise men saw where the baby born,
The wise men saw where the baby born,
And they say that his name was Jesus.
*He came from the glory...*

# JUST ANOTHER STAR

Carol Barratt
Karl Jenkins

2. Just another candle in the night,
   Just another shelter out of sight,
   Just another shepherd passin' by,
   Sheep stood round the manger listenin' to a lullaby.
   It was such a special place to stay,
   It was such a happy Christmas Day,
   It was such a glowing star that shone
   Up above the stable, where the Holy Child was born.
      *Love isn't ever far . . .*

# SLEIGH RIDE

Adapted from Czerny's piano reduction of a German Dance for Orchestra (K.605) by
**Wolfgang Amadeus Mozart** (1756 – 91).

# A STARRY NIGHT

**Words and music:
Joy Webb**

Chorus

*mf*

And all the an-gels sang for him _____ The bells of hea-ven rang for him, _____

D        D7        G

For a boy was born        King of all the world. _____

D        A7        D

And all the an-gels sang for him _____ The bells of hea-ven rang for him, _____

D        D7        G

For a boy was born        King of all the world. _____

D        A7        ( )

2. Soon the shepherds came that way
   Where the baby lay
   And were kneeling, kneeling by his side,
   And their hearts believed again
   For the peace of men,
   For a boy was born King of all the world.
       *And all the angels sang for him . . .*

# WHEN SANTA GOT STUCK UP THE CHIMNEY

**Words and music by
Jimmy Grafton**

# CHRISTMAS CARILLON

**Carol Barratt**

# AS I SAT ON A SUNNY BANK

**Words: Traditional**

**Music: Carol Barratt**

This **D** can be omitted if
turning the page yourself.